Every week Mrs May took some of the children to the swimming pool. The children were good swimmers and they liked going with Mrs May.

The children were taking a swimming test.

"It's time to begin," said Mrs May. "Who wants to go first?"

"We do," said Nadim.

Biff, Chip, Wilma, and Nadim jumped
into the pool. The water was warm.
"Off you go," called Mrs May.

They had to swim up and down the pool. They had to swim ten lengths. Wilma was first to swim ten lengths and Biff and Nadim were next.

It was hard for Chip to swim the ten
lengths.

"Come on, Chip," called Mrs May.
"Don't stop. This is the last length."
So Chip went on and everyone was pleased.

Next they had to swim to the bottom of
the pool. They had to pick up a brick and
swim with it to the top.

All the children passed the swimming test. Mrs May was very pleased.

"Well done, everyone," she said.

The children were pleased too.

Biff and Chip told Mum and Dad about the swimming test.

"We passed," they said.

Mum and Dad were very pleased too.

Mum and Dad had a surprise for them.
Biff and Chip couldn't see what the
surprise was.

"What is it?" asked Biff.

"It's a fish tank," said Biff. "What a lovely surprise!"
Everyone looked at the fish swimming about in the tank.

"There is room for more fish," said Dad.
"We can get some next time we go
shopping."

The next day they went shopping. Dad took them to a shop that sold fish.

"What a lovely shop!" said Biff. "Look at all the fish."

There were big fish and little fish. Kipper
liked the big fish in a tank.

"Don't tap the glass," said Dad. "The
fish don't like it."

Dad put some more fish in the tank. He put rocks on the bottom. Next to the rocks he put a ship and a little box.

Wilma and Nadim came to see the fish tank.

"It looks lovely," said Wilma. "I wish I could swim in there."

They went to play in Biff's room. Chip
ran in with the magic key. The key was
glowing.

"It's time for an adventure," said Biff.

The magic began to work. It took the
children into a new adventure. This time it
was a different sort of adventure.

The magic took them underwater. The children had masks and flippers and tanks of air. They could swim underwater.

The children had never seen so many fish. They were all different colours.

"This is better than the pool," thought Chip.

"I feel like a fish," thought Wilma.

The children loved swimming under the water. It was lovely to see all the fish and to swim with them.

Chip and Nadim swam to the bottom
and picked up a big shell. Biff looked at a
jellyfish but she didn't swim too close.

They saw a ship under the water. It was an old ship that had been under the water for a long time.

They swam up to the ship. Wilma didn't want to swim too close to it. It looked dangerous.

They saw an octopus. Oh no! It was
sitting on a chest. They couldn't look inside
the chest with an octopus sitting on the lid.

They blew bubbles at the octopus. The
octopus didn't like the bubbles so it swam
away.

"Good!" thought the children. "Now we
can look inside."

The children opened up the chest and
looked inside. It was a treasure chest and it
was full of gold.

Biff and Wilma pushed the chest over
and all the gold fell out. Nadim picked up
a necklace and Biff picked up a gold cup.

Biff and Nadim were busy looking at the treasure. They didn't see what Chip and Wilma saw. A shark was coming.

Chip and Wilma couldn't tell Biff and
Nadim. They pulled them away and
pointed at the shark.

The children were frightened. They swam and swam but the shark swam after them. Then the magic key began to glow.

The magic key took them out of the
adventure.

"Wow! What an adventure!" said Biff. "The
treasure chest was like the one in our fish
tank."

The children ran to look in the fish tank.
"Look, there's the treasure," said Chip.
"How did it get there?" asked Nadim.
"It's magic!" said Biff.